ADDRESSES

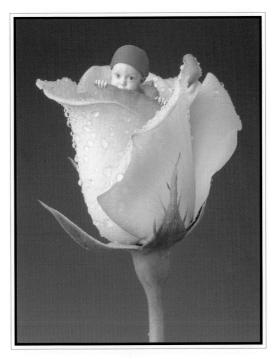

Images by

ANNE GEDDES

ISBN 1-55912-000-2

© Anne Geddes 1994

Published in 1995 by Cedco Publishing Company,
2955 Kerner Blvd, San Rafael, CA 94901.

First USA edition, January 1995
Second printing, February 1995

Designed by Jane Seabrook
Produced by Kel Geddes
Color separations by Metro Repro
Artwork by Bazz 'n' Else
Printed through Colorcraft, Hong Kong

Anne Geddes, an Australian-born photographer, resident in Auckland, New Zealand, has won the hearts of people internationally with her unique and special images of children.

Not only is her work widely recognized and sought after in the commercial field, but her exceptional images have received resounding critical acclaim, attracting a host of professional awards.

Many of Anne's distinctive and memorable photographs have been published internationally, including the prestigious USA's *"Life"* Magazine, Germany's *"Tempo"*, the *"London Sunday Mirror"* and The News of the World *"Sunday Magazine"* to name but a few.

Anne's work mirrors the joy and love found in the children who will form the future of the planet. After all, she says, *"To be able to capture on film the innocence, trust and happiness that is inherent in the next generation is a very special responsibility. It's work that rewards me daily with a great deal of personal satisfaction."*

Another major challenge in Anne's life is to ensure that the photography of children is widely accepted as an art form that legitimately competes with any other form of photographic speciality.

Anne is married to her friend and business partner Kel. Together they have two children.

A

Name_____

Address_____

_____

Phone_____

Name_____

Address_____

_____

Phone_____

Name_____

Address_____

_____

Phone_____

Name_____

Address_____

_____

Phone_____

A

Name

Address

Phone

Name

Address

Phone

Name

Address

Phone

Name

Address

Phone

A

Name_____

Address_____

_____

Phone_____

Name_____

Address_____

_____

Phone_____

Name_____

Address_____

_____

Phone_____

Name_____

Address_____

_____

Phone_____

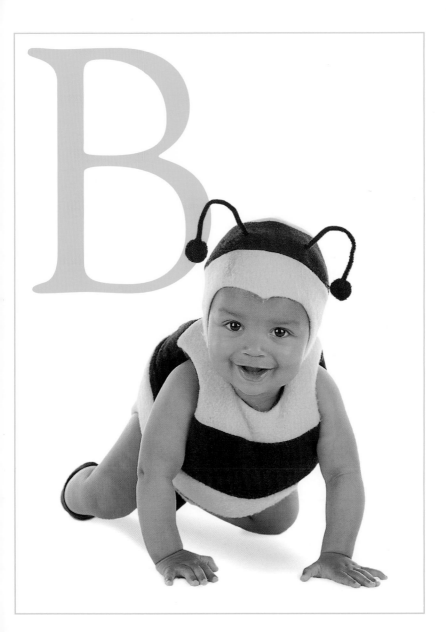

B

Name _____

Address _____

_____

Phone _____

Name _____

Address _____

_____

Phone _____

Name _____

Address _____

_____

Phone _____

Name _____

Address _____

_____

Phone _____

B

Name_____

Address_____

_____

Phone_____

Name_____

Address_____

_____

Phone_____

Name_____

Address_____

_____

Phone_____

Name_____

Address_____

_____

Phone_____

B

Name _____

Address _____

_____

Phone _____

Name _____

Address _____

_____

Phone _____

Name _____

Address _____

_____

Phone _____

Name _____

Address _____

_____

Phone _____

C

Name _____

Address _____

_____

Phone _____

Name _____

Address _____

_____

Phone _____

Name _____

Address _____

_____

Phone _____

Name _____

Address _____

_____

Phone _____

C

Name _____

Address _____

_____

Phone _____

Name _____

Address _____

_____

Phone _____

Name _____

Address _____

_____

Phone _____

Name _____

Address _____

_____

Phone _____

C

Name _____

Address _____

_____

Phone _____

Name _____

Address _____

_____

Phone _____

Name _____

Address _____

_____

Phone _____

Name _____

Address _____

_____

Phone _____

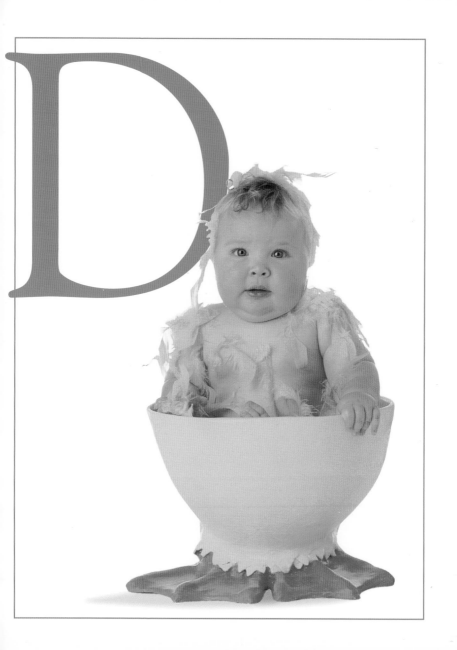

D

Name

Address

Phone

Name

Address

Phone

Name

Address

Phone

Name

Address

Phone

D

Name _____

Address _____

_____

Phone _____

Name _____

Address _____

_____

Phone _____

Name _____

Address _____

_____

Phone _____

Name _____

Address _____

_____

Phone _____

D

Name

Address

Phone

Name

Address

Phone

Name

Address

Phone

Name

Address

Phone

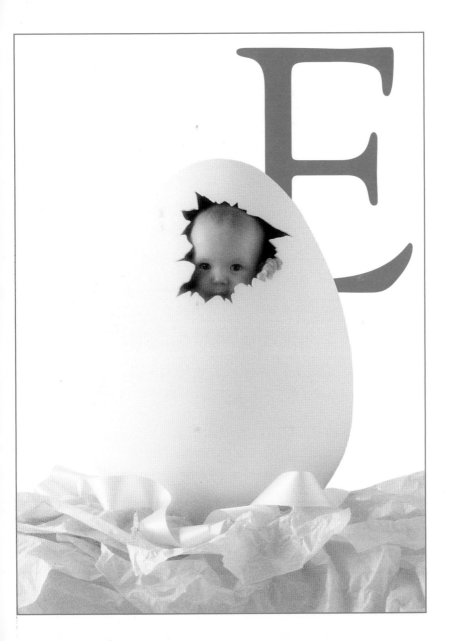

E

Name

Address

Phone

Name

Address

Phone

Name

Address

Phone

Name

Address

Phone

E

Name

Address

Phone

Name

Address

Phone

Name

Address

Phone

Name

Address

Phone

E

Name _____

Address _____

_____

Phone _____

Name _____

Address _____

_____

Phone _____

Name _____

Address _____

_____

Phone _____

Name _____

Address _____

_____

Phone _____

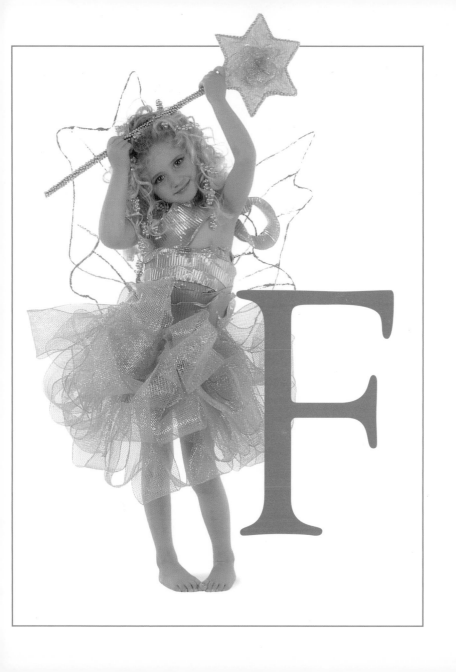

F

Name

Address

Phone

Name

Address

Phone

Name

Address

Phone

Name

Address

Phone

F

Name

Address

Phone

Name

Address

Phone

Name

Address

Phone

Name

Address

Phone

F

Name

Address

Phone

Name

Address

Phone

Name

Address

Phone

Name

Address

Phone

G

Name

Address

Phone

Name

Address

Phone

Name

Address

Phone

Name

Address

Phone

G

Name

Address

Phone

Name

Address

Phone

Name

Address

Phone

Name

Address

Phone

G

Name _____

Address _____

_____

Phone _____

Name _____

Address _____

_____

Phone _____

Name _____

Address _____

_____

Phone _____

Name _____

Address _____

_____

Phone _____

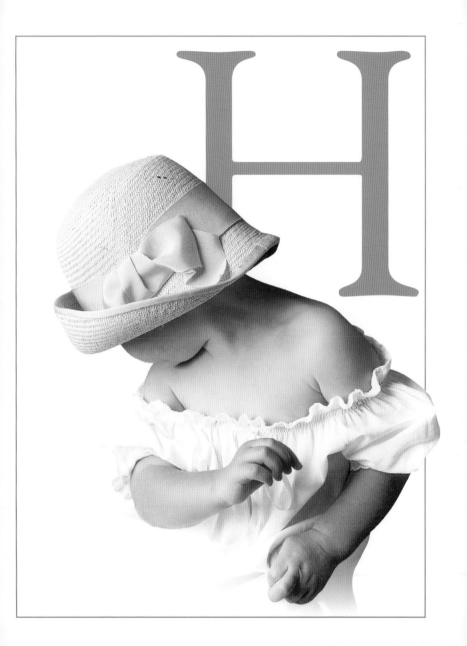

H

Name

Address

Phone

Name

Address

Phone

Name

Address

Phone

Name

Address

Phone

H

Name

Address

Phone

Name

Address

Phone

Name

Address

Phone

Name

Address

Phone

H

Name _____

Address _____

_____

Phone _____

Name _____

Address _____

_____

Phone _____

Name _____

Address _____

_____

Phone _____

Name _____

Address _____

_____

Phone _____

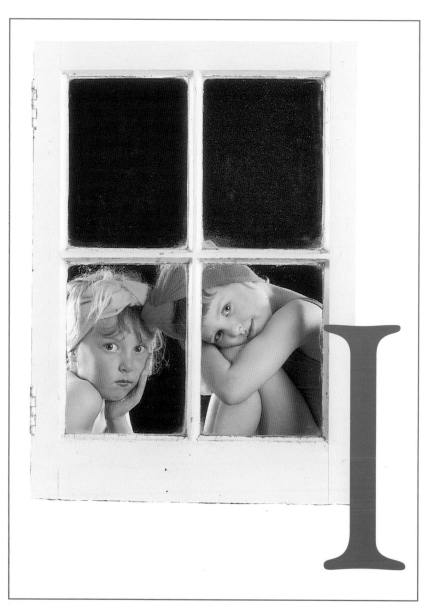

I

I

Name

Address

Phone

Name

Address

Phone

Name

Address

Phone

Name

Address

Phone

J

Name

Address

Phone

Name

Address

Phone

Name

Address

Phone

Name

Address

Phone

J

Name _____

Address _____

_____

Phone _____

Name _____

Address _____

_____

Phone _____

Name _____

Address _____

_____

Phone _____

Name _____

Address _____

_____

Phone _____

J

Name

Address

Phone

Name

Address

Phone

Name

Address

Phone

Name

Address

Phone

K

Name

Address

Phone

Name

Address

Phone

Name

Address

Phone

Name

Address

Phone

K

Name

Address

Phone

Name

Address

Phone

Name

Address

Phone

Name

Address

Phone

K

Name

Address

Phone

Name

Address

Phone

Name

Address

Phone

Name

Address

Phone

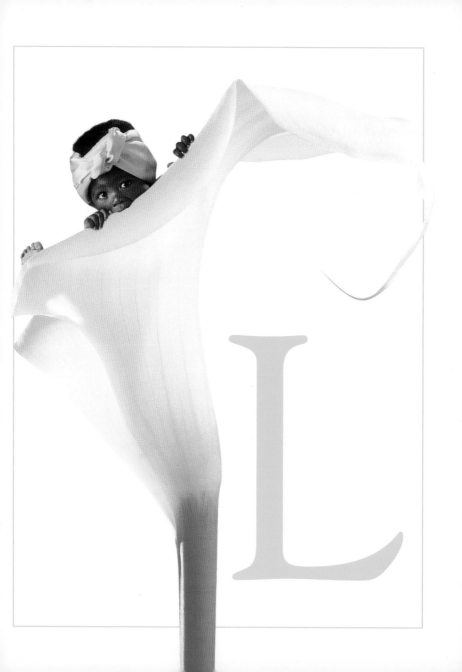

L

Name

Address

Phone

Name

Address

Phone

Name

Address

Phone

Name

Address

Phone

L

Name_____

Address_____

_____

Phone_____

Name_____

Address_____

_____

Phone_____

Name_____

Address_____

_____

Phone_____

Name_____

Address_____

_____

Phone_____

L

Name

Address

Phone

Name

Address

Phone

Name

Address

Phone

Name

Address

Phone

M

Name _____

Address _____

_____

Phone _____

Name _____

Address _____

_____

Phone _____

Name _____

Address _____

_____

Phone _____

Name _____

Address _____

_____

Phone _____

M

Name

Address

Phone

Name

Address

Phone

Name

Address

Phone

Name

Address

Phone

M

Name_____

Address_____

_____

Phone_____

Name_____

Address_____

_____

Phone_____

Name_____

Address_____

_____

Phone_____

Name_____

Address_____

_____

Phone_____

N

Name _____

Address _____

_____

Phone _____

Name _____

Address _____

_____

Phone _____

Name _____

Address _____

_____

Phone _____

Name _____

Address _____

_____

Phone _____

N

Name

Address

Phone

Name

Address

Phone

Name

Address

Phone

Name

Address

Phone

N

Name

Address

Phone

Name

Address

Phone

Name

Address

Phone

Name

Address

Phone

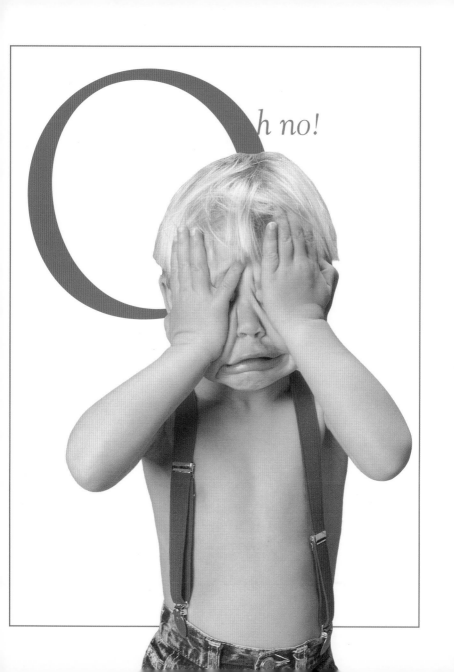

Oh no!

O

Name

Address

Phone

Name

Address

Phone

Name

Address

Phone

Name

Address

Phone

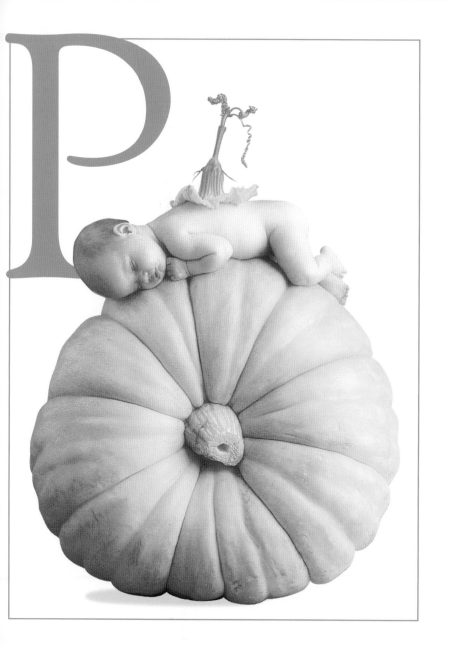

P

Name

Address

Phone

Name

Address

Phone

Name

Address

Phone

Name

Address

Phone

P

Name

Address

Phone

Name

Address

Phone

Name

Address

Phone

Name

Address

Phone

P

Name

Address

Phone

Name

Address

Phone

Name

Address

Phone

Name

Address

Phone

Name

Address

Phone

Name

Address

Phone

Name

Address

Phone

Name

Address

Phone

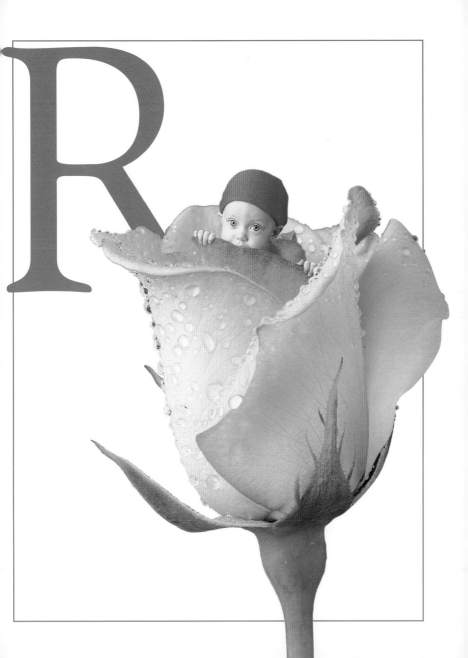

R

Name

Address

Phone

Name

Address

Phone

Name

Address

Phone

Name

Address

Phone

R

Name_____

Address_____

_____

Phone_____

Name_____

Address_____

_____

Phone_____

Name_____

Address_____

_____

Phone_____

Name_____

Address_____

_____

Phone_____

R

Name

Address

Phone

Name

Address

Phone

Name

Address

Phone

Name

Address

Phone

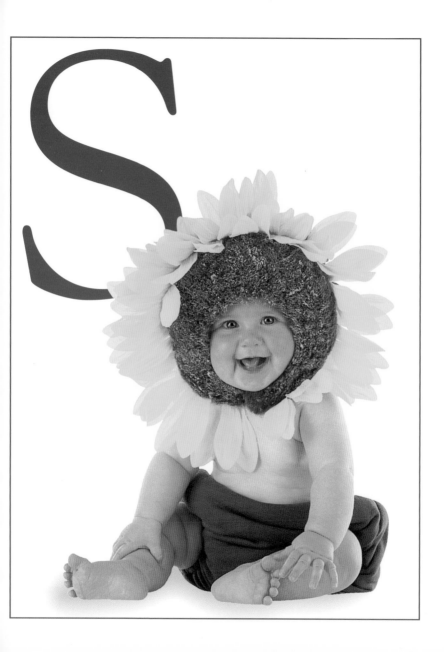

S

Name

Address

Phone

Name

Address

Phone

Name

Address

Phone

Name

Address

Phone

S

Name

Address

Phone

Name

Address

Phone

Name

Address

Phone

Name

Address

Phone

S

Name

Address

Phone

Name

Address

Phone

Name

Address

Phone

Name

Address

Phone

T

Name

Address

Phone

Name

Address

Phone

Name

Address

Phone

Name

Address

Phone

T

Name _____

Address _____

_____

Phone _____

Name _____

Address _____

_____

Phone _____

Name _____

Address _____

_____

Phone _____

Name _____

Address _____

_____

Phone _____

T

Name _____

Address _____

_____

Phone _____

Name _____

Address _____

_____

Phone _____

Name _____

Address _____

_____

Phone _____

Name _____

Address _____

_____

Phone _____

U

Name

Address

Phone

Name

Address

Phone

Name

Address

Phone

Name

Address

Phone

V

Name

Address

Phone

Name

Address

Phone

Name

Address

Phone

Name

Address

Phone

Name

Address

Phone

Name

Address

Phone

Name

Address

Phone

Name

Address

Phone

Name

Address

Phone

Name

Address

Phone

Name

Address

Phone

Name

Address

Phone

Name

Address

Phone

Name

Address

Phone

Name

Address

Phone

Name

Address

Phone

XYZ

Name

Address

Phone

Name

Address

Phone

Name

Address

Phone

Name

Address

Phone

XYZ

Name _____

Address _____

_____

Phone _____

Name _____

Address _____

_____

Phone _____

Name _____

Address _____

_____

Phone _____

Name _____

Address _____

_____

Phone _____